COMMON CORE CLINICS

Grade 4

Mathematics

Measurement, Data, and Geometry

Common Core Clinics, Mathematics, Measurement, Data, and Geometry, Grade 4
OT313 / 405NA

ISBN: 978-0-7836-8493-2

Author: Ann Petroni-McMullen
With special thanks to mathematics consultants:
Debra Harley, Director of Math/Science K–12, East Meadow School District
Allan Brimer, Math Specialist, New Visions School, Freeport School District
Cover Image: © herreid/Veer

Triumph Learning® 136 Madison Avenue, 7th Floor, New York, NY 10016

ALL ABOUT YOUR BOOK

COMMON CORE CLINICS MATH will help you with key concepts.

A **Key Words** box introduces new math words. An **Example** shows you how to solve problems in the lesson.

Each lesson has **Guided Practice**. Hints called **THINK** and **REMEMBER** help you work through the problem.

There are two pages of **Independent Practice** with problems for you to solve on your own. You will also solve some **Word Problems**.

At the back of your book, there is a **Glossary** and **Math Tools** that will help you work out problems.

Module 4

Measurement, Data, and Geometry

You can add, subtract, multiply, or divide to solve problems involving money. When you compute with money, remember to write the dollar sign and the decimal point in the answer. The decimal point separates the dollars from the cents.

Example

Georgia bought 6 tubes of paint for $31.50. Each tube of paint cost the same amount. How much did one tube of paint cost?

Choose the operation.
Each of 6 tubes of paint cost the same amount. The total is $31.50.
Divide to find the cost of one tube of paint.

Divide: $31.50 ÷ 6

Write the decimal point above the decimal point in the dividend.

$$6\overline{)31.50}$$

Divide as with whole numbers.

```
      5.25
  6)31.50
   -30
   ‾‾‾‾
     1 5
    -1 2
    ‾‾‾‾
       30
      -30
      ‾‾‾
        0
```

$31.50 ÷ 6 = $5.25

One tube of paint cost $5.25.

COMPARE

How is dividing with money amounts similar to dividing with whole numbers? How is it different?

Guided Practice

Quinn bought a skateboard for $45.95 and a helmet for $32.50, including tax.
He paid for the items with four $20 bills. How much change should Quinn receive?

Step 1 Find the total cost of the skateboard and the helmet.

Add: $45.95 + $32.50

Write the addends vertically, and add as with whole numbers.

$$\$\ 4\ 5\ .\ 9\ 5$$
$$+\ \ 3\ 2\ .\ 5\ 0$$
$$\$\ \boxed{}\boxed{}\ .\ \boxed{}\boxed{}$$

> **REMEMBER**
> Line up the money amounts by the decimal point to add or subtract. Then add or subtract from right to left.

Step 2 Find how much money Quinn used to pay for the items.

Multiply: 4 × $20.00

Write the factors vertically, and multiply as with whole numbers.

$$\$20.00$$
$$\times\qquad 4$$
$$\overline{\$80.00}$$

> **THINK**
> A $20 bill is 20 dollars and 0 cents. Write 20 dollars using a dollar sign and a decimal point. $20 = $20.00

Step 3 Subtract the total cost from the amount Quinn used to pay for the items.

Subtract: $80.00 − $78.45

Write the problem vertically, and subtract as with whole numbers.

$$\$\ 8\ 0\ .\ 0\ 0$$
$$-\ \ 7\ 8\ .\ 4\ 5$$
$$\$\ \ \boxed{}\ .\ \boxed{}\boxed{}$$

> **REMEMBER**
> Regroup as needed.

Quinn should receive _____ in change.

Independent Practice

1. Explain how to add, subtract, multiply, and divide with money amounts.

   _____

   _____

2. Why is it necessary to include the decimal point in money amounts that represent dollars and cents?

   _____

   _____

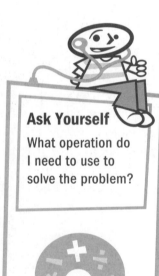

Ask Yourself

What operation do I need to use to solve the problem?

Add, subtract, multiply, or divide to find each answer.

3. $64.50
    + 12.95
    _____

4. $17.28
    − 9.34
    _____

5. $5.72
    ×   6
    _____

6. $17.44 ÷ 8 = _____

7. $74.67 − $12.99 = _____

8. $5.34 ÷ 6 = _____

9. Jasmine bought 8 pairs of socks. Each pair cost $3.45. How much did the socks cost in all?

   _____

10. Giorgio saved $8.25 from his allowance last week. This week, he saved $6.95 from his allowance. How much more did Giorgio save last week than this week?

    _____

Solve each problem.

11. For lunch, Andrea buys a sandwich for $3.60, an orange for $0.85, and a granola bar for $1.39. How much does Andrea spend on her lunch in all?

   _____

12. Chad bought a bag containing 5 tennis balls for $5.45. How much did each tennis ball cost?

   _____

13. Nora buys 3 pounds of grapes and 2 pounds of apples. The grapes cost $2.05 per pound, and the apples cost $1.14 per pound. How much do the grapes and apples cost in all?

   _____

14. Danny buys a pair of running shoes that are on sale for $12.99 off the regular price. He uses a coupon for $5.00 off when he pays for the shoes. The regular price of the shoes is $74.67. How much does Danny pay for the running shoes?

   _____

15. The basketball team raised $64.50 washing cars. They will use the money to buy new jerseys for the 8 players on the team. The jerseys cost $19.24 each. How much more money does the team need to raise to pay for the jerseys?

   _____

16. Neil bought 4 pounds of potatoes. He paid with a $10.00 bill and received $4.20 in change. How much did Neil pay for 1 pound of potatoes?

   _____

2 Time

Key Words

day (d)
hour (hr)
minute (min)
second (sec)

Units of time include **days**, **hours**, **minutes**, and **seconds**. You can use time equivalents to compute with time.

Units of Time
1 minute (min) = 60 seconds (sec)
1 hour (hr) = 60 minutes
1 day (d) = 24 hours

You can use addition, subtraction, multiplication, and division to solve problems about time. You can convert from a larger unit of time to a smaller unit of time.

Example

How many seconds are equal to 5 minutes?

Use the relationship between seconds and minutes.

1 minute = 60 seconds

Multiply each minute by the equivalent number of seconds.

1 minute = 60 seconds
2 minutes = 2 × 60 = 120 seconds
3 minutes = 3 × 60 = 180 seconds
4 minutes = 4 × 60 = 240 seconds
5 minutes = 5 × 60 = 300 seconds

Show the equivalent units in a table.

Minutes	Seconds
1	60
2	120
3	180
4	240
5	300

DEMONSTRATE

How many seconds are in 6 minutes? Find your answer two different ways.

You can also add to find the number of seconds in 5 minutes.

60 + 60 + 60 + 60 + 60 = 300

There are 300 seconds in 5 minutes.

Guided Practice

1 How many minutes are in $\frac{3}{4}$ hour?

> **Step 1** Use the relationship between minutes and hours.
>
> 1 hour = 60 minutes, so $\frac{3}{4}$ of 1 hour = $\frac{3}{4}$ of 60 minutes.
>
> **Step 2** Multiply to find the number of minutes in $\frac{3}{4}$ hour.
>
> $$\frac{3}{4} \times 60 = \frac{3 \times 60}{4} = \frac{180}{4}$$
>
> $$= \underline{\hspace{2cm}}$$

> **REMEMBER**
>
> To multiply a fraction and a whole number, multiply the whole number by the numerator of the fraction. Write the product over the denominator of the fraction.

> **Step 3** Write the equivalent times.
>
> $\frac{3}{4}$ hour = _____ minutes
>
> There are _____ minutes in $\frac{3}{4}$ hour.

2 Emmet spent 40 minutes washing his car, 30 minutes mowing the lawn, and 25 minutes paying bills. How much time these chores take?

> **Step 1** Write an addition equation to show the situation.
>
> Use t to represent the total amount of time.
>
> $40 + 30 + 25 - t$

> **Step 2** Add to find the total number of minutes.
>
> $40 + 30 + 25 = \underline{\hspace{2.5cm}}$

> **THINK**
>
> Use the equivalence 1 hr = 60 min. Subtract 60 minutes as many times as possible to find the number of hours in 95 minutes.

> **Step 3** Write the sum as hours and minutes.
>
> $95 - 60 = \underline{\hspace{2.5cm}}$
>
> 95 minutes = _____ hour _____ minutes

These chores took _____ minutes, or _____ hour _____ minutes.

Independent Practice

1. How do you convert from days to hours?

   _____

   _____

2. How do you convert from hours to minutes?

   _____

   _____

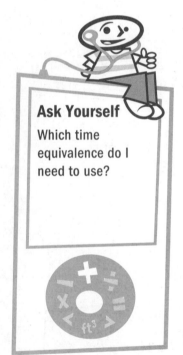

Ask Yourself

Which time equivalence do I need to use?

Complete each equivalent statement.

3. 5 hr = _____ min

4. 7 min = _____ sec

5. 2 min = _____ sec

6. 48 hr = _____ d

7. 3 d = _____ hr

8. 10 min = _____ sec

9. 240 min = _____ hr

10. 3 hr = _____ min

11. 3 min = _____ sec

12. $\frac{1}{2}$ hr = _____ min

13. A dance class lasts for 60 minutes. How many hours long is the dance class?

    _____

14. Cindy rode the bus for $\frac{1}{4}$ hour. For how many minutes did Cindy ride the bus?

    _____

Use equivalent units of time to complete the tables.

15.

Hours	Minutes
1	
2	
3	
4	
5	
6	
7	

16.

Days	Hours
1	
2	
3	
4	
5	
6	
7	

Solve each problem.

17. Gus spent 3 hours 25 minutes at the science fair. How many minutes did Gus spend at the science fair?

_____

18. Angie spent 2 hours at the science museum. She spent $\frac{3}{4}$ of her time at the dinosaur exhibit. For how long was Angie at the dinosaur exhibit?

_____

19. Bryce catches the bus for school at 8:15 A.M. He spends 20 minutes eating, 10 minutes dressing, and 15 minutes cleaning up before he leaves for the bus. It takes him 5 minutes to walk to the bus. What is the latest time Bryce can get up to be on time for the bus?

_____

3 Weight and Mass

Key Words

gram (g)
kilogram (kg)
ounce (oz)
pound (lb)

The customary units of weight include the **pound** and the **ounce**.

Units of Weight
1 pound (lb) = 16 ounces (oz)

The metric units of mass include the **kilogram** and the **gram**.

Units of Mass
1 kilogram (kg) = 1,000 grams (g)

You can use addition, subtraction, multiplication, and division to solve problems about weight or mass. You can multiply to convert from a larger unit of weight or mass to a smaller unit of weight or mass.

Example

Summer bought 2 kilograms of red potatoes, 950 grams of russet potatoes, and 875 grams of sweet potatoes. How many grams of potatoes did she buy?

Add to find the total. The units must be the same to add.
Convert 2 kilograms to grams so all the units are grams.
Use the relationship between grams and kilograms.

1 kilogram = 1,000 grams

Multiply the number of kilograms by 1,000, the equivalent number of grams.

1 kilogram = 1,000 grams
2 kilograms = 2 × 1,000 g = 2,000 g

2 kilograms = 2,000 grams

Add to find the total number of grams.

```
  1 1
  2,000
    950
+   875
  3,825
```

Summer bought 3,825 grams of potatoes.

EXPLAIN

Would a greater number of ounces or pounds be needed to measure the weight of an elephant? Explain your answer.

12

Guided Practice

1 How many ounces are equal to 5 pounds?

 Step 1 Use the relationship between pounds and ounces.

 1 pound = 16 ounces

 Step 2 Complete the table. Multiply each number of pounds by the equivalent number of ounces.

> **THINK**
> You could also add 16 to the previous total for each additional pound.

Pounds	Ounces
1	16
2	32
3	48
4	
5	

 _____ ounces = 5 pounds

2 An oatmeal factory has 2,144 kg of oats to pack into bags. Each bag holds 8 kg of oats. How many bags are needed to pack all the oats?

 Step 1 Write a division equation for the situation.

 Use b to represent the number of bags needed.

 $2,144 \div 8 = b$

 Step 2 Divide.

 $8\overline{)2,144}$

> **THINK**
> You are dividing kilograms by kilograms. The answer is not in kilograms. The answer is the number of bags needed.

 _____ bags of oats are needed.

Independent Practice

1. How do you convert from kilograms to grams?

_____

_____

2. When you convert from a larger unit, such as pounds, to a smaller unit, such as ounces, will the number of smaller units be greater than or less than the number of larger units? Explain.

_____

_____

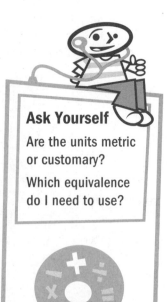

Ask Yourself

Are the units metric or customary?

Which equivalence do I need to use?

Complete each equivalent statement.

3. 3 lb = _____ oz

4. 6 lb = _____ oz

5. 8 lb = _____ oz

6. 2 lb 9 oz = _____ oz

7. 4 lb 3 oz = _____ oz

8. 4 kg = _____ g

9. 2,000 g = _____ kg

10. 9 kg = _____ g

11. Each ball in a bag of 6 balls has the same mass. The total mass of the balls is 810 grams. What is the mass of each ball?

_____

12. Betsy's puppy weighed 14 pounds in April. By June, her puppy gained 46 ounces. How much did Betsy's puppy weigh in June? Express the answer in pounds and ounces.

_____

Use equivalent units of weight and mass to complete the tables.

13.

Pounds	Ounces
6	
7	
8	
9	
10	

14.

Kilograms	Grams
1	
2	
3	
4	
5	

Solve each problem.

15. Devin bought a pumpkin and a squash. The pumpkin had a mass of 9 kilograms. The squash had a mass of 470 grams. How much greater was the mass of the pumpkin than the mass of the squash?

_____

16. Ian buys 4 bags of apples. Each bag of apples weighs 3 pounds. How many ounces of apples does Ian buy?

_____

17. Two rocks in Olivia's collection have a total mass of 2 kilograms. One of the rocks has a mass of 940 grams. What is the mass of the other rock?

_____

18. Ron buys 2 pounds of peanuts, 5 ounces of cashews, 8 ounces of pecans, 12 ounces of almonds, and 1 pound 3 ounces of walnuts. What is the total weight of the nuts Ron buys?

_____

4 Capacity

Capacity, or **liquid volume**, is the amount of liquid that a container can hold. **Cups, pints, quarts,** and **gallons** are the customary units of capacity.

Customary Units of Capacity
1 pint (pt) = 2 cups (c) 1 quart (qt) = 2 pints 1 gallon (gal) = 4 quarts

Milliliters and **liters** are metric units of capacity or liquid volume.

Metric Units of Capacity
1 liter (L) = 1,000 milliliters (mL)

You can use addition, subtraction, multiplication, and division to solve problems about capacity. You can multiply to convert from a larger unit of capacity to a smaller unit of capacity.

Example

Felipe makes 3 pints of yogurt. He will put the yogurt into 1-cup containers. How many containers can Felipe fill?

Find the number of cups in 3 pints.

Convert 3 pints to cups.
Use the relationship between cups and pints.

1 pint = 2 cups

Multiply the number of pints by 2 to find the equivalent number of cups.

1 pint = 2 cups
3 pints = 3 × 2 cups = 6 cups

Felipe can fill 6 containers.

DEDUCE

How would you find the number of quarts in 20 gallons? Explain.

Guided Practice

1 A bucket holds 5 liters of water. Paige pours 2,300 milliliters of water into the bucket. How much more water can the bucket hold?

Step 1 Subtract to find how much more water is needed.

Subtract: 5 L − 2,300 mL

Step 2 The units must be the same to subtract.

1 L = 1,000 mL

5 L = 5 × 1,000 mL = _____ mL

THINK

A liter is a larger unit than a milliliter. Multiply to find the number of milliliters in 5 liters.

Step 3 Subtract to find the difference.

_____ − 2,300 = _____

The bucket can hold _____ milliliters more of water.

2 Each person in Mr. Kline's family drinks $\frac{2}{3}$ pint of milk each day. There are 4 people in Mr. Kline's family. How many pints of milk does Mr. Kline need to have for his family for Monday?

Step 1 Write a multiplication equation for the situation.

Use m to represent the number of pints of milk.

$4 \times \frac{2}{3} = m$

THINK

You can also add:

$\frac{2}{3} + \frac{2}{3} + \frac{2}{3} + \frac{2}{3} = m$

Step 2 Multiply to find the total number of pints.

$4 \times \frac{2}{3} = \frac{4 \times 2}{3}$

$= \frac{\square}{3}$

$= \square\frac{\square}{\square}$

REMEMBER

To multiply a fraction and a whole number, multiply the whole number by the numerator of the fraction. Write the product over the denominator.

Mr. Kline needs _____ pints of milk for Monday.

Independent Practice

1. What is capacity?

_____

_____

2. How could you convert from gallons to pints?

_____

_____

Ask Yourself

Which equivalence do I need to use?

Complete each equivalent statement.

3. 4 pt = _____ c

4. 8 qt = _____ pt

5. 3 gal = _____ qt

6. 8 gal = _____ pt

7. 16 pt = _____ c

8. 24 gal = _____ qt

9. 9 pt = _____ c

10. 6 L = _____ mL

11. 8 qt = _____ c

12. 10 L = _____ mL

13. Bridget tries to drink 2 quarts of water every day. Today she has had 3 pints of water. How much more water does Bridget need to drink to reach her goal?

_____

14. Chloe needs 3 quarts of broth to make soup. She has a measuring cup with a capacity of 1 pint. How many times must she fill the cup to measure enough broth for her soup?

_____

Use equivalent units of capacity to complete the tables.

15.

Gallons	Quarts
1	
2	
3	
4	
5	
6	
7	

16.

Quarts	Pints
1	
2	
3	
4	
5	
6	
7	

Solve each problem.

17. In science class, Arnold poured 97 milliliters of red-tinted water into a 1-liter jar. Then he filled the jar with blue-tinted water. How much blue-tinted water did Arnold pour into the jar?

_____

18. For a birthday party, Mrs. Kelly plans to fill each of 8 glasses with 200 milliliters of punch. The punch is sold in 1-liter bottles. How many bottles of punch does Mrs. Kelly need? Explain.

_____

19. An aquarium holds 10 gallons of water. How many full pitchers of water will Dai use to fill the aquarium if he uses a 2-quart pitcher to fill it?

_____

Inches, **feet**, **yards**, and **miles** are customary units of length.

Customary Units of Length
1 foot (ft) = 12 inches (in.)
1 yard (yd) = 3 feet
1 mile (mi) = 5,280 ft

Centimeters, **meters**, and **kilometers** are metric units of length.

Metric Units of Length
1 meter (m) = 100 centimeters (cm)
1 kilometer (km) = 1,000 meters

You can use addition, subtraction, multiplication, and division to solve problems about length. You can multiply to convert from a larger unit of length to a smaller unit of length.

Key Words

centimeter (cm)
foot (ft)
inch (in.)
kilometer (km)
meter (m)
mile (mi)
yard (yd)

Example

Akira needs 1 foot of ribbon for each banner she makes. The ribbon is sold by the inch. How many inches of ribbon does Akira need to make 5 banners?

Find the amount of ribbon Akira needs.
Multiply 1 foot for each banner by 5 banners: $1 \times 5 = 5$

Akira needs 5 feet of ribbon.

Find the number of inches in 5 feet.
Make a table. Use the relationship between feet and inches. 1 foot = 12 inches

Feet	Inches
1	12
2	24
3	36
4	48
5	60

Think: $1 \times 12 = 12$
Think: $2 \times 12 = 24$
Think: $3 \times 12 = 36$
Think: $4 \times 12 = 48$
Think: $5 \times 12 = 60$

EXPLAIN

Would measuring the distance between cities take a greater number of yards or a greater number of miles? Explain your answer.

Akira needs 60 inches of ribbon to make 5 banners.

Guided Practice

 Leon walks 3 kilometers every morning. So far this morning, he has walked 1,800 meters. How much farther does Leon need to walk this morning?

Step 1 Subtract to find how much farther Leon has to walk.

Subtract: 3 km − 1,800 meters

Step 2 The units must be the same to subtract.

1 km = 1,000 m

3 km = 3 × 1,000 m = 3,000 m

THINK

A kilometer is a larger unit than a meter.

Multiply to find the number of meters in 3 kilometers.

Step 3 Subtract to find the difference.

_____ − 1,800 = _____

Leon needs to walk _____ more meters this morning.

2 Sally walks $\frac{3}{8}$ mile from her home to the bus stop each morning. She walks the same distance in the evening. How many miles is Sally's round-trip to and from the bus stop each day?

Step 1 Add to find the total distance.

Add: $\frac{3}{8} + \frac{3}{8}$

$$\frac{3}{8} + \frac{3}{8} = \frac{\square}{\square}$$

THINK

The distance Sally walks is the same each way, so you can also multiply $2 \times \frac{3}{8}$.

Step 2 Write an equivalent fraction for the sum.

$$\frac{\square}{\square} = \frac{\square}{4}$$

REMEMBER

To add fractions with the same denominator, add the numerators. Write the sum over the denominator.

Sally walks _____ mile each day to and from the bus stop.

Independent Practice

1. How could you convert from yards to inches?

_____

_____

2. How is changing from meters to centimeters different than changing from kilometers to meters?

_____

_____

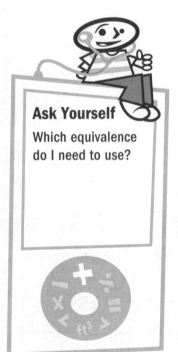

Ask Yourself

Which equivalence do I need to use?

Complete each equivalent statement.

3. 4 yd = _____ ft

4. 3 ft = _____ in.

5. 2 mi = _____ ft

6. 3 yd = _____ ft

7. 8 ft = _____ in.

8. 9 km = _____ m

9. 5 m = _____ cm

10. 30 m = _____ cm

11. 72 km = _____ m

12. 60 km = _____ m

13. A blue whale is 78 feet long. How many inches is 78 feet?

_____

14. A strip of land 5 kilometers long is divided into 4 sections of the same length. How many meters long is each section?

_____

Use equivalent units of length to complete the tables.

15.

Yards	Feet
1	
2	
3	
4	
5	
6	

16.

Meters	Centimeters
1	
2	
3	
4	
5	
6	

Solve each problem.

17. Lauren is 50 inches tall. Her mother is 5 feet 6 inches tall. How much taller is Lauren's mother?

_____

18. A beetle is 2 centimeters long. A snake is 100 times as long as the beetle. How many meters long is the snake?

_____

19. A spool has 5 meters of tubing. Owen cuts off a piece that is 225 centimeters long. How much tubing is left on the spool?

_____

20. Nevena has a board that is 4 feet long. She cuts the entire board into pieces that are 8 inches long. How many pieces does she cut?

_____

6 Perimeter

Key Words

perimeter

Perimeter is the measure of the distance around a figure. To find the perimeter of a rectangle, you can add the lengths of the sides. Another way to find the perimeter of a rectangle is to use this formula:

Perimeter = (2 × length) + (2 × width) or $P = (2 \times l) + (2 \times w)$

Example

A rectangular window is 7 feet long and 3 feet wide. What is the perimeter of the window?

3 ft

7 ft

Write the formula for the perimeter of a rectangle.

$P = (2 \times l) + (2 \times w)$

In the formula for the perimeter of a rectangle, replace *l* with 7 and *w* with 3.

$P = (2 \times 7) + (2 \times 3)$

Find the perimeter.

$P = (2 \times 7) + (2 \times 3)$

$P = 14 + 6$

$P = 20$

The perimeter of the window is 20 feet.

DEMONSTRATE

Why is the formula for the perimeter of a rectangle the same as adding the lengths of the sides of a rectangle?

Guided Practice

The perimeter of a rectangular mat is 36 inches. The mat is 10 inches long. How wide is the mat?

10 inches

? inches

Step 1 Write the formula for the perimeter of a rectangle.

$P = (2 \times l) + (2 \times w)$

Step 2 In the formula for the perimeter of a rectangle, write what you know from the problem.

_____ = (2 × _____) + (2 × w)

> **THINK**
> You know that the perimeter is 36 inches and the length is 10 inches. Replace *P* with 36 and *l* with 10.

Step 3 Solve the equation.

36 = (2 × _____) + (2 × w)

= (_____) + (2 × w)

The total of the lengths is _____ inches.

> **THINK**
> A rectangle has 2 sides that are called the length. Both lengths are a total of 20 inches. Subtract from the perimeter to find the total of the widths.

Step 4 Subtract the total of the lengths from the perimeter.

36 − 20 = 16

The total of the widths is _____ inches.

Step 5 Divide the total of both widths to find each width.

16 ÷ 2 = _____

Each width is _____ inches.

> **THINK**
> A rectangle has 2 sides that are called the width. 16 inches is the total of both widths and is what (2 × *w*) represents in the formula.

The width of the mat is _____ inches.

Independent Practice

1. Explain how to use a formula to find the perimeter of a rectangle.

_____

_____

2. The perimeter of a rectangle is a measurement. How do you know which units to use to label the perimeter?

_____

_____

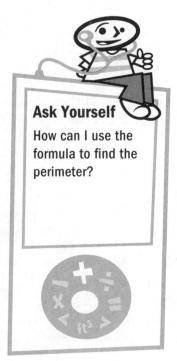

Ask Yourself

How can I use the formula to find the perimeter?

Find the perimeter of each rectangle.

3.
12 m

5 m

P = _____

4.
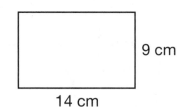
9 cm

14 cm

P = _____

5.
 2 yd

21 yd

P = _____

6.
38 in.

38 in.

P = _____

7. A rectangular sandbox is 9 feet long and 6 feet wide. What is the perimeter of the sandbox?

_____

Solve each problem.

8. A square lot has sides that are 32 meters long. What is the perimeter of the lot?

_____

9. A rectangular rug is 96 inches long and 65 inches wide. What is the perimeter of the rug?

_____

10. A rectangular blanket is 70 inches long and 48 inches wide. Kim wants to put a border along the edge of the blanket. What is the least amount of ribbon Kim needs to go around the edge of the blanket?

_____

11. The perimeter of a rectangular tablecloth is 26 feet. The tablecloth is 8 feet long. How wide is the tablecloth?

_____

12. The perimeter of a square scarf is 100 inches. How long is each side of the scarf?

_____

13. A rectangular garden is 28 meters long and 7 meters wide. A farmer wants to enclose the garden with a fence. How many meters of fence does the farmer need to enclose the garden?

_____

Key Words

area

Area is the size of a region inside a figure. It is measured in square units. A square unit is a square with a side length of 1 unit.

To find the area of a rectangle, you can count the number of square units that cover the rectangle. Another way to find the area of a rectangle is to use this formula:

Area = length × width or $A = l \times w$

Example

A rectangular rug is 9 feet long and 6 feet wide. What is the area of the rug?

9 ft

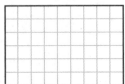

6 ft

Write the formula for the area of a rectangle.

$A = l \times w$

In the formula for the area of a rectangle, replace l with 9 and w with 6.

$A = 9 \times 6$

Find the area.

$A = 9 \times 6$

$A = 54$

Label the area with the units used in the problem.

The length and width of the rug are in feet. Label the area of the rug in square feet.

The area of the rug is 54 square feet.

LABEL

What unit would you use to label the area of a picture that is 5 inches wide and 7 inches long?

Guided Practice

The area of a rectangular garden is 225 square meters. The garden is 9 meters wide. How long is the garden?

? m

9 m

Step 1 Write the formula for the area of a rectangle.

$A = l \times w$

Step 2 In the formula, write what you know from the problem.

_____ = $l \times$ _____

Step 3 Solve the equation.

$225 = l \times 9$

Divide: $225 \div 9$

$9\overline{)225}$

Step 4 Label the answer.

$l =$ _____

The garden is _____ meters long.

Independent Practice

1. What is area?

_____

_____

2. Explain how to use a formula to find the area of a rectangle.

_____

_____

Ask Yourself

What units do I use to label the area?

Find the area of each rectangle.

3.

16 m

7 m

A = _____

4.

3 yd

18 yd

A = _____

5.

43 ft

43 ft

A = _____

6.

26 m

5 m

A = _____

7. A rectangular flower garden is 7 meters long and 4 meters wide. What is the area of the flower garden?

_____

Solve each problem.

8. A square field has sides that are 34 yards long.
    What is the area of the field?

    _____

9. A rectangular poster is 64 centimeters long and
    38 centimeters wide. What is the area of the poster?

    _____

10. A rectangular mat is 21 inches long and 16 inches wide.
    What is the area of the mat?

    _____

11. The area of a rectangular curtain is 60 square feet.
    The curtain is 5 feet wide. How long is the curtain?

    _____

12. The area of a square tablecloth is 36 square feet.
    How long is each side of the tablecloth?

    _____

13. A rectangular garden is 8 feet long and 6 feet wide.
    A bag of topsoil covers 3 square feet. How many
    bags of topsoil are needed to cover the garden?

    _____

8 Angles

Key Words

angle
degree
protractor
ray
vertex

A **ray** is part of a line that starts at one endpoint and goes on without end in the other direction. An **angle** is formed by two rays that meet at the same endpoint. The common endpoint is called a **vertex**.

An angle is measured in **degrees (°)**. One degree is an angle that turns through $\frac{1}{360}$ of a circle. A full turn around a circle is 360°.

The measure of an angle is the number of 1-degree angles through which it turns. For example, an angle with a measure of 40 degrees turns through 40 1-degree angles.

A **protractor** is a tool used to measure an angle. The scale on a protractor is marked from 0° to 180°.

Example

Use a protractor to draw an angle that measures 55°.

Draw a ray with an endpoint.

Place the center mark of the protractor on the endpoint of the ray and align the 0° mark with the ray.

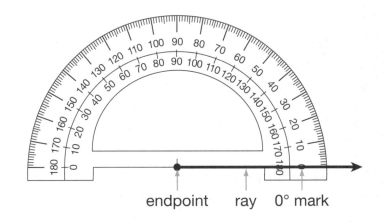

endpoint   ray   0° mark

Mark a point at 55°.

Draw a second ray from the endpoint through the point at 55°.

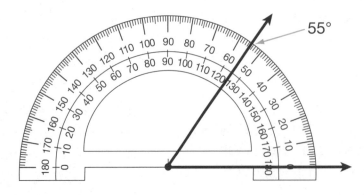

55°

The angle above measures 55°.

INTEGRATE

If an angle that measures 15° is added to the 55° angle in the example, what is the measure of the new angle that is formed?

Guided Practice

1 Use a protractor to measure the angle.

Step 1 Place the center mark of the protractor on the vertex of the angle. Line up the center point and the 0° mark on the protractor with one ray of the angle.

Step 2 Find where the other ray passes through the scale on the protractor.

Use the scale that makes sense for the angle.

THINK

The angle is greater than 90°. Use the scale that shows a measure greater than 90° at the point where the ray crosses it.

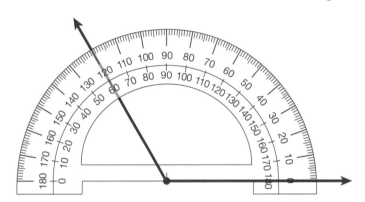

The measure of the angle is _____.

2 What is the measure of angle *ABC* if the measure of angle *ABD* is 60°?

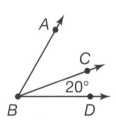

Step 1 Write an equation to find the unknown angle measure.

angle *ABD* − angle *CBD* = angle *ABC*
     60°   −   20°   =   ?

Step 2 Subtract to find the measure of angle *ABC*.

60° − 20° = _____

REMEMBER

An angle is named by its sides and by its endpoint. When naming an angle, the vertex is the middle letter.

The measure of angle *ABC* is _____.

33

Independent Practice

1. Through how many 1-degree angles does a 38° angle turn? Explain.

   _____

   _____

2. How do you decide which scale to use when you use a protractor to draw or measure an angle?

   _____

   _____

Ask Yourself

After I line up one ray with the 0° mark on the protractor, where does the other ray cross the scale on the protractor?

Use a protractor to measure each angle.

3.

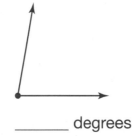

_____ degrees

4.

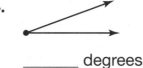

_____ degrees

5.

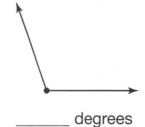

_____ degrees

6.

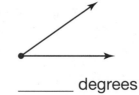

_____ degrees

7.

_____ degrees

8.

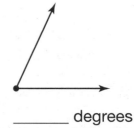

_____ degrees

Use a protractor to draw an angle with each measure.

9. 70°

10. 40°

11. 100°

12. 130°

13. 60°

14. 120°

15. What is the measure of angle *QRT* if the measure of angle *SRT* is 25°?

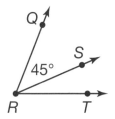

_____

16. What is the measure of angle *CDF* if the measure of angle *EDF* is 15°?

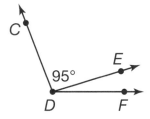

_____

17. What is the measure of angle *JKL* if the measure of angle *JKM* is 45°?

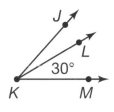

_____

18. What is the measure of angle *ABC* if the measure of angle *ABD* is 105°?

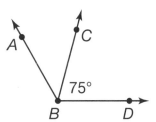

_____

Solve.

19. The hands on a clock form an angle that measures 60°.
If the minute hand is at 12, what time could it be?

_____

A **line plot** is a graph that uses a number line to show the number of times data occur. An X or a dot is used to record each data point.

Example 1

Randy keeps track of the length of each beetle in his collection. He measures each beetle to the nearest $\frac{1}{4}$ inch. He records the following lengths:

$$\frac{1}{4}, \frac{1}{4}, \frac{3}{4}, \frac{2}{4}, \frac{2}{4}, \frac{3}{4}, \frac{1}{4}, \frac{2}{4}, 1, \frac{1}{4}, \frac{1}{4}, \frac{3}{4}, 1, \frac{2}{4}$$

Make a line plot to show Randy's data.

Make a number line. Divide the number line into fourths.

Put an X above a number each time that length occurs in Randy's list. Give the line plot a title.

Lengths of Beetles (in inches)

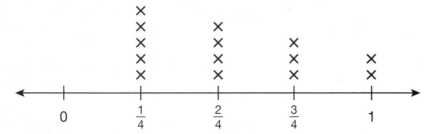

Example 2

How many beetles does Randy have that are $\frac{1}{4}$-inch long?

Use the line plot.
Count the number of Xs above $\frac{1}{4}$.

There are 5 Xs above $\frac{1}{4}$.

Randy has 5 beetles that are $\frac{1}{4}$-inch long.

INTERPRET

How many beetles does Randy have that are $\frac{1}{2}$-inch long? Explain.

Guided Practice

The line plot shows the heights of plants students are growing in their science class. The students measured the heights of the plants to the nearest $\frac{1}{6}$ foot.

Heights of Plants (in feet)

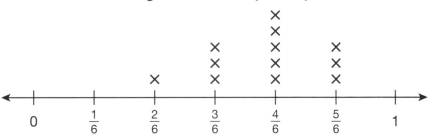

What is the difference in height between the tallest plants and the shortest plants? How many plants are greater than $\frac{1}{6}$ foot high and less than $\frac{5}{6}$ foot high?

Step 1 Find the height of the tallest plant.

The tallest plant is _____ foot.

> **REMEMBER**
> The greatest number lies to the right on a number line.

Step 2 Find the height of the shortest plant.

The shortest plant is _____ foot.

Step 3 Find the difference in the heights.

_____ − _____ = _____

The difference between the tallest and shortest

plants is _____ foot.

> **REMEMBER**
> To subtract fractions with like denominators, subtract the numerators and write the difference over the same denominator.

Step 4 Decide which of the fractions are greater than $\frac{1}{6}$ and less than $\frac{5}{6}$.

The fractions greater than $\frac{1}{6}$ and less than $\frac{5}{6}$ are _____.

Step 5 Count the number of Xs above each fraction listed in Step 4. Add the numbers.

_____ + _____ + _____ = _____

There are _____ plants that are greater than $\frac{1}{6}$ foot high and less than $\frac{5}{6}$ foot high.

Independent Practice

1. Explain how a line plot shows data.

_____

2. How do you make a line plot that shows fractional measurements?

_____

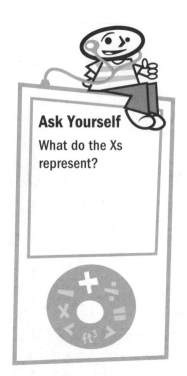

Ask Yourself

What do the Xs represent?

Use the line plot to answer questions 3 through 6.

The line plot shows the weights of clay figures students made at a craft party.

Weights of Clay Figures (in pounds)

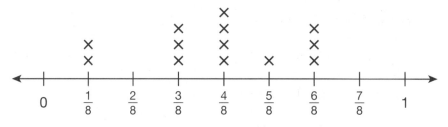

3. What is the weight of the greatest number of figures?

_____

4. How many figures did the students make in all?

_____

5. What is the difference in weight between the lightest and the heaviest figures?

_____

6. How much clay did the students use to make all the figures that weigh $\frac{4}{8}$ pound? Explain.

_____

7. Ben keeps track of the number of cups of milk he uses to make different batches of muffins. He records the following amounts:

$$\frac{3}{4}, \frac{3}{4}, \frac{2}{4}, \frac{3}{4}, \frac{3}{4}, \frac{1}{4}, \frac{2}{4}, \frac{3}{4}, \frac{2}{4}, \frac{1}{4}, \frac{2}{4}$$

a. Make a line plot to show Ben's data.

b. How many batches of muffins did Ben make that used milk?

_____

c. How many times did Ben make muffins using at least $\frac{2}{4}$-cup of milk?

_____

8. A scientist collects spiders. The lengths, in inches, of her spiders are:

$$\frac{5}{8}, \frac{7}{8}, \frac{4}{8}, \frac{5}{8}, \frac{6}{8}, \frac{3}{8}, \frac{2}{8}, \frac{7}{8}, \frac{4}{8}, \frac{6}{8}, \frac{7}{8}, \frac{6}{8}, \frac{3}{8}, \frac{4}{8}, \frac{2}{8}, \frac{6}{8}, \frac{3}{8}, \frac{7}{8}, \frac{5}{8}, \frac{4}{8}, \frac{6}{8}$$

a. Make a line plot to show the spider length data.

b. How much longer is the longest spider than the shortest spider in the collection?

_____

10 Lines and Angles

You can use the definitions of geometric figures to draw and identify the figures.

A **point** is a location in space. A **line** is a straight path that goes on without end in two directions. A **line segment** is part of a line and has two endpoints. You can name a line or a line segment by the points on the line or line segment.

Parallel lines are always the same distance apart. **Perpendicular lines** form right angles.

A **right angle** forms a square corner and has a measure of 90°. An **acute angle** has a measure less than 90°. An **obtuse angle** has a measure greater than 90° and less than 180°.

Key Words

acute angle
line
line segment
obtuse angle
parallel lines
perpendicular
 lines
point
right angle

Example

Draw a pair of parallel lines and a pair of perpendicular lines.

Use the definitions to draw the lines.

Parallel lines are always the same distance apart.
Use a ruler to draw two straight lines that are always the same distance apart.

Perpendicular lines form right angles.

Use a ruler to draw a horizontal line and a vertical line that cross. Use a square to show that the lines meet to form right angles.

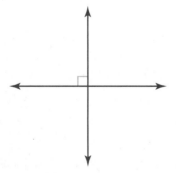

SELECT

Look around your classroom. Identify items that contain a pair of parallel lines and a pair of perpendicular lines. Explain how you know the lines are parallel and perpendicular.

Guided Practice

Name the angle in three different ways. Then classify the angle as acute, right, or obtuse.

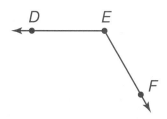

Step 1 Name the angle by its endpoint.

∠E

Step 2 Use the sides to name the angle.

∠DEF or ∠FED

Step 3 Classify the angle.

Does the angle form a square corner? _____

Is the angle a right angle? _____

Is the angle less than a right angle? _____

Is the angle an acute angle? _____

Is the angle greater than a right angle? _____

Is the angle an obtuse angle? _____

Three different ways to name the angle are _____,

_____, and _____.

The angle is a(n) _____ angle.

REMEMBER
You can name an angle using only the vertex.

THINK
You can name an angle using a point on one ray, the vertex, and a point on the other ray.

THINK
Compare the angle to a right angle.
An acute angle is less than a right angle.
An obtuse angle is greater than a right angle.

Independent Practice

1. How is a line different than a line segment?

_____

_____

2. Explain the difference between parallel lines and perpendicular lines.

_____

_____

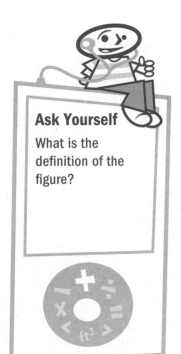

Ask Yourself

What is the definition of the figure?

Draw an example of each geometric figure.

3. line *FG*

4. point *P*

5. right angle *JKL*

6. ray *QR*

7. acute angle *ABC*

8. line segment *ST*

9. obtuse angle *LMN*

10. parallel lines

11. perpendicular lines

Name each figure. If it is an angle, state if the angle is acute, right, or obtuse.

12.

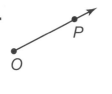

_____

13.

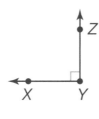

_____

14.

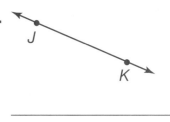

_____

15.

_____

16.

_____

17.

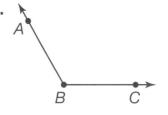

_____

Use the figure below to answer questions 18 through 22.

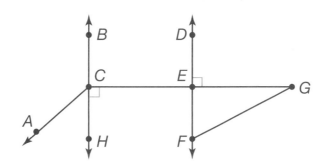

18. Name a pair of parallel lines. _____

19. Name a pair of perpendicular lines or line segments. _____

20. Name three line segments. _____

21. Name two rays. _____

22. Name an obtuse angle. _____

11 Two-Dimensional Shapes

Key Words

quadrilateral
rectangle
right triangle
square
triangle

A **triangle** is a figure with 3 sides and 3 angles. If one of the angles is a right angle, the triangle is called a **right triangle**.

A **quadrilateral** is a figure with 4 sides and 4 angles. A **rectangle** is a quadrilateral with two pairs of parallel sides, opposite sides that are equal in length, and 4 right angles. A **square** is a rectangle with 4 equal sides.

Example

Classify the figure below. Then describe the figure.

Count the number of sides and angles the figure has.

The figure has 4 sides and 4 angles.

Classify the figure.

The figure is a quadrilateral.

Describe the sides of the figure.

The opposite sides of the quadrilateral are parallel.

The opposite sides are equal in length.

Describe the angles of the figure.

The quadrilateral has 2 acute angles and 2 obtuse angles.

Is the quadrilateral a rectangle or a square? No.

The figure is a quadrilateral with opposite sides that are parallel and equal in length. It has 2 acute angles and 2 obtuse angles.

CONCLUDE

The quadrilateral in the example has two pairs of parallel sides and opposite sides that are equal in length, but it is not a rectangle. Why?

Guided Practice

Classify the figure below. Then describe the figure.

Step 1 Count the number of sides and angles the figure has.

The figure has _____ sides and _____ angles.

Step 2 Classify the figure.

The figure is a _____.

Step 3 Describe the sides of the figure.

Are any of the sides parallel? _____

Are any of the sides perpendicular? _____

Step 4 Describe the angles of the figure.

How many acute angles does the figure have? _____

How many right angles does the figure have? _____

How many obtuse angles does the figure have? _____

Step 5 Decide if the figure is a special triangle or quadrilateral.

Is the figure a right triangle? _____

The figure is a _____. It has _____ right angle,

so it is a _____.

> **REMEMBER**
> Use the number of sides and angles to classify the figure.

> **THINK**
> Perpendicular sides meet to form right angles.

Independent Practice

1. If a figure has parallel sides, how can this help you classify the figure?

_____

_____

2. How does the size of the angles in a figure help you classify the figure?

_____

_____

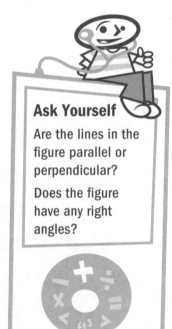

Ask Yourself

Are the lines in the figure parallel or perpendicular?

Does the figure have any right angles?

Classify each figure. Be as specific as possible.

3.

_____

4.

_____

5.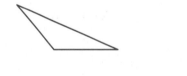

_____

6.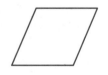

_____

7.

_____

8.

_____

Classify each figure. Then describe the relationships between the sides of the figure. Also, describe the types of angles the figure has.

9.

_____

_____

_____

10.

_____

_____

_____

11.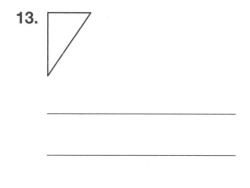

_____

_____

_____

12.

_____

_____

_____

13.

_____

_____

14.

_____

_____

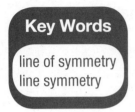

12 Symmetry

A figure has **line symmetry** if it can be folded along a line so that the two halves match exactly. This line is called the **line of symmetry**.

Figures can have one or more lines of symmetry. Some figures have no lines of symmetry.

Example

Does the figure below have line symmetry? If so, draw all the lines of symmetry.

Find whether the figure can be folded in half so that the two parts match exactly.

Can the rectangle be folded in half across a vertical line?

Yes, the rectangle can be folded in half across a vertical line.

Can the rectangle be folded in half across a horizontal line?

Yes, the rectangle can be folded in half across a horizontal line.

The rectangle has line symmetry. It has two lines of symmetry as shown above.

DISTINGUISH

Is a diagonal line a line of symmetry for a rectangle? Explain.

Guided Practice

How many lines of symmetry does the triangle have?

Step 1 Divide the figure in half along a vertical line.

THINK

How can the figure be folded so the parts match exactly?

Step 2 Check for another line of symmetry.

THINK

Can the figure be folded in other places so the parts match exactly?

Step 3 Check for another line of symmetry.

Step 4 Decide if there are any other lines of symmetry.

Are there any other lines of symmetry? _____

The triangle has _____ lines of symmetry.

Independent Practice

1. How can you tell if a figure has line symmetry?

_____

_____

2. Explain how to draw a line of symmetry.

_____

_____

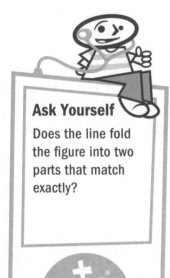

Ask Yourself

Does the line fold the figure into two parts that match exactly?

Is the dashed line a line of symmetry? Write _yes_ or _no_.

3.

_____

4.

_____

5.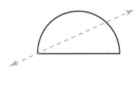

_____

6.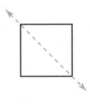

_____

7.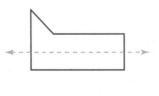

_____

8.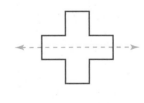

_____

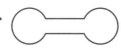
Draw all the lines of symmetry for each figure.

9.

10.

11.

12.

13.

14.

Solve each problem.

15. What is a letter of the alphabet that has more than one line of symmetry? What is a letter with no lines of symmetry? Explain.

_____

_____

16. A designer uses the flower designs shown below.

    A   B   C   D

   a. Do all of the flowers have a line of symmetry? _____

   b. Do any of the flowers have more than one line of symmetry?
      If so, which one(s)?

      _____

Glossary

acute angle an angle with a measure less than 90° (Page 40)

angle a figure formed by two rays with a common endpoint (Page 32)

area the number of square units needed to cover a surface (Page 28)

capacity the measure of how much liquid a container can hold (Page 16)

centimeter (cm) a metric unit of length; 100 centimeters = 1 meter (Page 20)

cup (c) a customary unit of capacity; 2 cups = 1 pint (Page 16)

day (d) a unit of time; 1 day = 24 hours (Page 8)

degree (°) a unit used to measure angles (Page 32)

foot (ft) a customary unit of length; 1 foot = 12 inches (Page 20)

gallon (gal) a customary unit of capacity; 1 gallon = 4 quarts (Page 16)

gram (g) a metric unit of mass; 1,000 grams = 1 kilogram (Page 12)

hour (hr) a unit of time; 1 hour = 60 minutes (Page 8)

inch (in.) a customary unit of length; 12 inches = 1 foot (Page 20)

kilogram (kg) a metric unit of mass; 1 kilogram = 1,000 grams (Page 12)

kilometer (km) a metric unit of length; 1 kilometer = 1,000 meters (Page 20)

line a straight path that goes in two directions without end (Page 40)

line of symmetry a line that divides a figure into two parts so that the parts match exactly (Page 48)

line plot a graph that uses Xs or dots above a number line to record data (Page 36)

line segment a part of a line, with two endpoints (Page 40)

line symmetry a property of a figure if it can be folded along a line so that its two halves match (Page 48)

liquid volume the measure of how much liquid a container can hold; also called capacity (Page 16)

liter (L) a metric unit of capacity; 1 liter = 1,000 milliliters (Page 16)

meter (m) a metric unit of length; 1 meter = 100 centimeters (Page 20)

mile (mi) a customary unit of length; 1 mile = 5,280 feet (Page 20)

milliliter (mL) a metric unit of capacity; 1,000 milliliters = 1 liter (Page 16)

minute (min) a unit of time; 60 minutes = 1 hour (Page 8)

obtuse angle an angle with a measure greater than 90° and less than 180° (Page 40)

ounce (oz) a customary unit of weight; 16 ounces = 1 pound (Page 12)

parallel lines lines that are always the same distance apart (Page 40)

perimeter the distance around a figure (Page 24)

perpendicular lines lines that cross and form right angles (Page 40)

pint (pt) a customary unit of capacity; 1 pint = 2 cups (Page 16)

point a location in space (Page 40)

pound (lb) a customary unit of weight; 1 pound = 16 ounces (Page 12)

protractor a tool used to measure an angle (Page 32)

quadrilateral a two-dimensional shape with 4 sides and 4 angles (Page 44)

quart (qt) a customary unit of capacity; 1 quart = 2 pints (Page 16)

ray a part of a line that starts at one endpoint and goes on without end in the other direction (Page 32)

rectangle a quadrilateral with two pairs of parallel sides, opposite sides that are equal in length, and 4 right angles (Page 44)

right angle an angle that measures exactly 90° (Page 40)

right triangle a triangle with one right angle (Page 44)

second (sec) a unit of time; 60 seconds = 1 minute (Page 8)

square a rectangle with 4 equal sides (Page 44)

triangle a two-dimensional shape with 3 sides and 3 angles (Page 44)

vertex the common endpoint where two rays meet to form an angle (Page 32)

yard (yd) a customary unit of length; 1 yard = 3 feet (Page 20)

Math Tools: Grid Paper

Cut or tear carefully along this line.

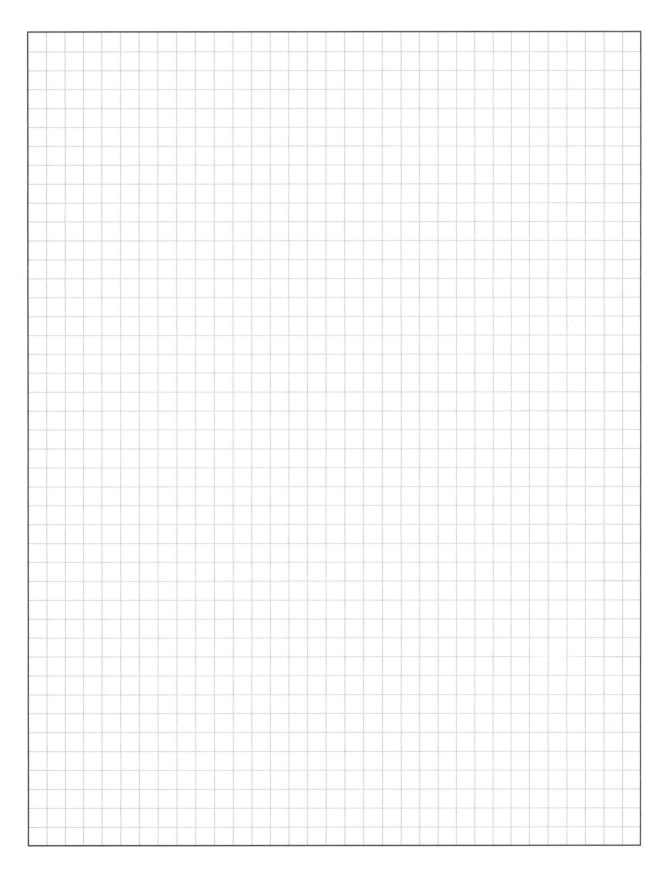